CAROLS FOR CHOIRS

FIFTY CHRISTMAS CAROLS

Edited and arranged by

REGINALD JACQUES
AND
DAVID WILLCOCKS

MUSIC DEPARTMENT

OXFORD UNIVERSITY PRESS

| 44 CONDUIT STREET | 417 FIFTH AVENUE |
| LONDON · W.1 | NEW YORK 16 · N.Y. |

CAROLS FOR CHOIRS

NOTE

THESE fifty Christmas carols, mostly for mixed voices, have been chosen and arranged with carol concerts and carol services in mind.

Many of the carols are from traditional sources and include a number of well-loved tunes either newly arranged by the present Editors or in settings by other distinguished musicians both past and present. A little more than half are for unaccompanied singing, the remainder having accompaniments for piano or organ and incorporating varied harmonizations and descants.

Four carols have been written specially for the book by Arnold Cooke, Reginald Jacques, Phyllis Tate, and William Walton; original compositions by Bach, Berlioz, Benjamin Britten, Armstrong Gibbs, John Joubert, and R. Vaughan Williams are also included.

The texts of the now traditional NINE LESSONS are printed as an Appendix, and a leaflet containing the words only of thirteen of the most popular carols, for the use of audiences and congregations, is on sale. The accompaniments to these thirteen carols (see Index) have been arranged for strings, the parts being on hire.

Carols for Choirs is a comprehensive and varied collection, and it is hoped that by using it choirs will be able to perform their Christmas concerts and services without the inconvenience of handling a number of separate leaflets and books.

Note on the NINE LESSONS

The service of Nine Lessons with Carols was first drawn up by Archbishop Benson when Bishop of Truro for use in that Cathedral, and was later simplified and modified for use in King's College Chapel, Cambridge, in 1918 by its then Dean, the Very Reverend Eric Milner-White, to whom also we owe the Bidding Prayer.

Engraved, printed lithographically, and bound in Holland by
KEESMAAT BROTHERS, HAARLEM

INDEX OF TITLES AND FIRST LINES

Where first lines differ from titles the former are shown in italics.

Carols suitable for unaccompanied singing are marked thus *.
Accompaniment for strings is available on hire †.

continued overleaf

INDEX OF TITLES AND FIRST LINES

The words of the following carols make up the congregation/audience words leaflet, published separately :

A GREAT AND MIGHTY WONDER
AS WITH GLADNESS MEN OF OLD
GOD REST YOU MERRY, GENTLEMEN
GOOD KING WENCESLAS
HARK! THE HERALD ANGELS SING
IT CAME UPON THE MIDNIGHT
  CLEAR

O COME, ALL YE FAITHFUL
O LITTLE TOWN OF BETHLEHEM
ONCE IN ROYAL DAVID'S CITY
SEE AMID THE WINTER'S SNOW
THE FIRST NOWELL
UNTO US IS BORN A SON
WHILE SHEPHERDS WATCHED
  THEIR FLOCKS

1. A GREAT AND MIGHTY WONDER

Words by St. GERMANUS (634-734)
tr. J. M. NEALE

Old German tune
harmonized by M. PRAETORIUS
(1571-1621)

The barring of this tune is necessarily irregular. But its performance will be found to be easy if it is remembered that the time-value of a crotchet is the same throughout.

3. While thus they sing your monarch,
   Those bright angelic bands,
   Rejoice, ye vales and mountains,
   Ye oceans clap your hands.
   Repeat the hymn again! etc.

4. Since all he comes to ransom,
   By all be he adored,
   The Infant born in Bethl'em
   The Saviour and the Lord.
   Repeat the hymn again! etc.

5. And idol forms shall perish,
   And error shall decay,
   And Christ shall wield his sceptre,
   Our Lord and God for ay.
   Repeat the hymn again! etc.

2. AWAY IN A MANGER

(First tune)

Words anon.

Tune by W.J. KIRKPATRICK (1838-1921)
arranged by DAVID WILLCOCKS

In verse 3 the whole choir may hum whilst a treble soloist sings the words.

2. AWAY IN A MANGER

(Second tune)

Words anon.

Traditional Normandy tune
arranged by REGINALD JACQUES

SOPRANO
ALTO

1. A - way in a man - ger, no crib for a bed, The
2. The cat - tle are low - ing, the ba - by a - wakes, But
3. Be near me, Lord Je - sus; I ask thee to stay Close

TENOR
BASS

lit - tle Lord Je - sus laid down his sweet head. The
lit - tle Lord Je - sus no cry - ing he makes. I
by me for e - ver, and love me, I pray. Bless

stars in the bright sky looked down where he lay, The
love thee, Lord Je - sus! Look down from the sky, And
all the dear chil - dren in thy ten - der care, And

lit - tle Lord Je - sus a - sleep on the hay.
stay by my side un - til morn - ing is nigh.
fit us for hea - ven, to live with thee there.

Melody reprinted from *University Carol Book* by permission of H. Freeman & Co.

To my father

3. A BOY WAS BORN

16th century
German words
Tr. PERCY DEARMER

BENJAMIN BRITTEN

This is the theme from the Choral Variations of the same title. (O.U.P.) The words are reprinted from *The Oxford Book of Carols* by permission.

-lu - ya,   Al - le - lu - ya,   Al - le - lu - - ya.   Then

-lu - ya,   Al - le - lu - ya,   Al - le - lu - - ya.   Then

-lu - ya,   Al - le - lu - ya,   Al - le - lu - - ya.   Then

-lu - ya,   Al - le - lu - ya,   Al - le - lu - - ya.   Then

praise   the   Word   of   God   who came   To   dwell with - in   a

praise   the   Word   of   God   who came   To   dwell with - in   a

praise   the   Word   of   God   who came   To   dwell with - in   a

praise   the   Word   of   God   who came   To   dwell with - in   a

4. AS WITH GLADNESS MEN OF OLD

Words by
W. CHATTERTON DIX

Abridged from a chorale, *Treuer Heiland*,
by C. KOCHER, 1786-1872
arranged by DAVID WILLCOCKS

1. As with glad-ness men of old   Did the guid-ing star be-hold,
As with joy they hailed its light, Lead-ing on-ward, beam-ing bright,

So, most gra-cious God, may we   Ev-er-more be   led   to   thee.

2. As with joyful steps they sped,
   To that lowly manger-bed,
   There to bend the knee before
   Him whom heaven and earth adore,
   So may we with willing feet
   Ever seek thy mercy-seat.

3. As they offered gifts most rare
   At that manger rude and bare,
   So may we with holy joy,
   Pure, and free from sin's alloy,
   All our costliest treasures bring,
   Christ, to thee our heavenly King.

4. Holy Jesu, every day
   Keep us in the narrow way;
   And, when earthly things are past,
   Bring our ransomed souls at last
   Where they need no star to guide,
   Where no clouds thy glory hide.

The harmonies used for verses 1-4 are from *The English Hymnal*. It is suggested that verse 4 is sung by the choir only, unaccompanied.

5. AND THERE WERE SHEPHERDS

J.S. BACH
(from *Christmas Oratorio*)
edited by DAVID WILLCOCKS

The words of the recitative are from Luke ii vv. 8-11

From bar 2 the accompaniment is as scored by Bach for strings (Bach's figures have been included so that the bass may be fully realised).

6. A VIRGIN MOST PURE

English traditional carol
arranged by CHARLES WOOD

1. A vir - gin most pure, as the pro - phets do tell, Hath brought forth a ba - by, as it hath be - fell; To be our Re - deem - er from_ death, hell, and_ sin, Which A - dam's trans - gres - sion had_ wrap-ped us_ in.

2. In Beth - le - hem Jew - ry a ci - ty there was, Where Jo - seph and Ma - ry to - geth - er did pass, And there to be tax - ed with_ ma - ny one_ mo, For Cae - sar com - mand - ed the_ same should be_ so. *Aye, and there - fore be*

* In verse 4 these slurred notes must be split
Reprinted from *The Cowley Carol Book* by permission

mer - ry; Re - joice, and be you mer - ry; Set— sor - row a -

- side; Christ Je - sus our Sa - viour was— born— at this— tide.

3. But when they had enter'd the city so fair,
   A number of people so mighty was there,
   That Joseph and Mary, whose substance was small,
   Could find in the inn there no lodging at all.
   Aye, and therefore, etc.

4. Then they were constrain'd in a stable to lie,
   Where horses and asses they us'd for to tie;
   Their lodging so simple they took it no scorn,
   But against the next morning our Saviour was born.
   Aye, and therefore, etc.

5. The King of all kings to this world being brought,
   Small store of fine linen to wrap him was sought;
   And when she had swaddled her young son so sweet,
   Within an ox-manger she laid him to sleep.
   Aye, and therefore, etc.

6. Then God sent an angel from heaven so high,
   To certain poor shepherds in fields where they lie,
   And bade them no longer in sorrow to stay,
   Because that our Saviour was born on this day.
   Aye, and therefore, etc.

7. Then presently after the shepherds did spy
   A number of angels that stood in the sky;
   They joyfully talkèd and sweetly did sing,
   'To God be all glory our heavenly King.'
   Aye, and therefore, etc.

7. ANGELS, FROM THE REALMS OF GLORY

Words by
J. MONTGOMERY

Old French tune
arranged by REGINALD JACQUES

Glo - - - - - - - - - - - - - -

Glo - - - - - - - - - - - - -

Glo - - - - - - - - - - - - - - - - - - -

- - ri - a

in   ex - cel - sis   De - - - - o.

- - ri - a

- - ri - a___

Montgomery's original words for the refrain were *Come and worship, Worship Christ the new-born King.*

3. Sages, leave your contemplations;
    Brighter visions beam afar;
  Seek the great desire of nations;
    Ye have seen his natal star:
      Gloria in excelsis Deo.

4. Saints before the altar bending,
    Watching long in hope and fear,
  Suddenly the Lord, descending,
    In his temple shall appear:
      Gloria in excelsis Deo.

5. Though an infant now we view him,
    He shall fill his Father's throne,
  Gather all the nations to him;
    Every knee shall then bow down:
      Gloria in excelsis Deo.

8. A CHRISTMAS CAROL

Words by
CLEMENT F. ROGERS

Hungarian traditional tune
arranged by ZOLTÁN KODÁLY

Fill   all our days,   Hear   us   when   we   call.

Fill   all our days,   Hear   us · when   we   call.

Fill   all   our   days,   Hear   us   when   we   call.

Fill   all   our days,   Hear   us   when   we   call.

A - - - - - - - - - - - - -

A - - - - - - - - -

A - - - - - - -

A - - -

- - - - - - - - - men.

- - - - - - - - - - men.

- - - - - - - - men.

- - - - - - - - men.

9. BLESSED BE THAT MAID MARY

Words by
G. R. WOODWARD

English traditional tune
arranged by DAVID WILLCOCKS

SOPRANO I
3. Sweet and bliss-ful was the_ song_ Chant-ed_of the_ an-gel_throng,

SOPRANO II
ALTO
"Peace on_earth", Al - le - lu - ya.__   In_ ex - cel - sis_ glo - ri - a.

In ex - cel - sis glo-ri-a. E - ya!

In ex - cel - sis glo - ri - a.__

E - ya! Je - sus ho - di - e__ Na-tus_est de_ vir-gi - ne.__

Je - sus ho - di - e__ Na - tus_ est de vir-gi - ne, de vir-gi - ne.

E - ya! Je - sus ho - di - e__ Na - tus, na-tus_est de vir-gi - ne.

TENOR
4. Fare three kings from far - off land,_ In-cense,gold and myrrh in_hand;

BASS I
BASS II
In_ Beth-lem the_ Babe they_ see, Stel - le_ duc-ti_ lu - mi - ne.

In_ Beth lem the_ Babe they see, Stel - le_ duc-ti lu-mi-ne.

In Beth-lem the Babe they see,__ Stel - le duc-ti lu - mi - ne.__

E - ya! Je - sus ho - di - e__ Na-tus_est de_ vir-gi - ne.__

E - ya! Je - sus ho - di - e Na - tus est de vir - gi - ne.

E - ya! Je - sus Na-tus_ est de_ vir - gi-ne.

(to next page)

CHOIR I

CHOIR II

To__ as - soil   and   save us__ all._____ E - ya! Je - sus

To__ as - soil__ and   save, and   save us   all.

ho - di - e _____ Na - tus est de vir - gi - ne._____

E - ya! Je - sus Na - tus est de vir - gi - ne.

Na - tus__ est de vir - - gi - ne.

E - ya! Je - sus

E - ya! Je - sus Na - tus est de vir - gi - ne.

E - ya! Je - sus Na - tus__ est de vir - - gi - ne.

10. DING DONG! MERRILY ON HIGH

Words by
G. R. WOODWARD

16th c. French tune
harmonized by CHARLES WOOD

1. Ding dong! mer-ri-ly on high   in heav'n the bells are ring-ing:
   Ding dong! ve-ri-ly the sky   is riv'n with an-gel sing-ing.

2. E'en so here be-low, be-low,   let stee-ple bells be swung-en,
   And i - o, i - o, i - o,   by priest and peo-ple sung-en.

3. Pray you, du-ti-ful-ly prime your mat-in chime, ye ring-ers;
   May you beau-ti-ful-ly rime your eve-time song, ye sing-ers.

Glo - - - - - - - - - - - -

- - - - - - - - - ri-a, Ho-san-na in ex-cel-sis!

i-o pronounced *ee-o*

Reprinted from *The Cambridge Carol Book* by permission

11. GOD REST YOU MERRY, GENTLEMEN

English traditional carol
arranged by DAVID WILLCOCKS

* If preferred, the refrain may always be sung in unison (with organ accompaniment)

Unison voices

3. The shepherds at those tidings
   Rejoicèd much in mind,
   And left their flocks a-feeding,
   In tempest, storm and wind,
   And went to Bethlehem straightway
   This blessèd babe to find:
   O tidings of comfort and joy.

Unaccompanied voices

4. But when to Bethlehem they came,
   Whereat this infant lay,
   They found him in a manger,
   Where oxen feed on hay;
   His mother Mary kneeling,
   Unto the Lord did pray:
   O tidings of comfort and joy.

SOPRANOS I II

Ah———————— Ah————————

ALTOS

TENORS and BASSES

5. Now to the Lord sing prais - es, All you with-in this place, And

ORGAN

Sw.

Gt.

Ped.

Ah———————— Ah———————— Ah————————

with true love and bro-ther-hood Each o-ther now em - brace; This ho - ly tide of

O— ti - dings of com - fort and

Christ-mas All o-thers doth de - face: O— ti - dings of com - fort and

Gt.

joy, com-fort and joy, O— ti - dings of com - fort and joy.

joy, com-fort and joy, O— ti - dings of com - fort and joy.

12. ZITHER CAROL

Words by
MALCOLM SARGENT

Czech folk tune
arranged by MALCOLM SARGENT

Girls and boys, leave your toys, make no noise,

Kneel at his crib and wor-ship him. At thy shrine, Child di-vine, we are thine,

*zing pronounced tzing
zm pronounced tzoomm

All slurred notes to be sung *legato* and with *glissando*

© 1958 Oxford University Press

Our Sa-viour's here. "Hal-le-lu-jah" the church-bells ring, "Hal-le-lu-jah" the

zm   zm— "Hal-le-lu-jah" the church-bells ring, "Hal-le-lu-jah" the

zing zing zing   zm—   zing zing   zing zing   zing zing
zing zing zing   zm—

zm   zm—   zing zing zing   zm—   zing zing zing

an-gels sing, "Hal-le-lu-jah" from ev-'ry-thing. All must draw near.

an-gels sing, "Hal-le-lu-jah" from ev-'ry-thing. All must draw near. Zing

zing zing   zing zing zing "Hal-le-lu-jah" from ev-'ry-thing. All must draw near. Zing
near. Zing

zm—   "Hal-le-lu-jah" from ev-'ry-thing. All must draw near.

2. _p_ On that day-far away-Jesus lay,
   Angels were watching round his head.
   Holy Child-Mother mild-undefiled,
   cresc. We sing thy praise.
       _f_ "Hallelujah" etc.
       Our hearts we raise.

3. _mf_ Shepherds came-at the fame-of thy name,
   Angels their guide to Bethlehem.
   In that place-saw thy face-filled with grace,
       Stood at thy door.
       _f_ "Hallelujah" etc.
       Love evermore.

4. _mf_ Wise men too-haste to do-homage new,
   Gold, myrrh and frankincense they bring.
   As 'twas said-starlight led-to thy bed,
       _p_ Bending their knee.
       _f_ "Hallelujah" etc.
       Worshipping thee.

5. _pp_ Oh, that we-all might be-good as he,
   Spotless, with God in Unity.
   cresc. Saviour dear-ever near-with us here
       Since life began.
       _f_ "Hallelujah" etc.
       Godhead made man.

6. _f_ Cherubim-Seraphim-worship him,
   Sun, moon and stars proclaim his power.
   Everyday-on our way-we shall say
       _ff_ Hallelujah.
       _ff_ "Hallelujah" etc.
       Hallelujah.

13. GOOD KING WENCESLAS

Words by J. M. NEALE

Tune from *Piae Cantiones*
arranged by REGINALD JACQUES

ORGAN or PIANO

SOPRANO ALTO

(ORGAN or PIANO)

TENOR BASS

1. Good King Wen-ces-las look'd out On the Feast of Ste - phen,

When the snow lay round a - bout, Deep, and crisp, and e - ven:

Bright-ly shone the moon that night, Though the frost was cru - el,

When a poor man came in sight, Ga-th'ring win-ter fu - - - el.

Note: The harmonies used for verse 1 and the second part of verse 3 are by Sir John Stainer (1840-1901)

© 1961 Oxford University Press

† small notes for piano

TENORS and BASSES

_mf_

3. 'Bring me flesh, and bring me wine, Bring me pine-logs hi - ther:

ORGAN or PIANO

_mf_

Thou and I will see him dine, When we bear them thi - ther.'

SOPRANO ALTO

_f_

(ORGAN or PIANO)

Page and mon-arch, forth they went, Forth they went to - ge - ther;

TENOR BASS

_f_

Through the rude wind's wild la - ment And the bit - ter wea - - ther.

4. 'Sire, the night is dar-ker now, And the wind blows stron - ger;

Fails my heart, I know not how; I can go no lon - ger.'

'Mark my foot-steps, good my page; Tread thou in them bold - ly:

Thou shalt find the win-ter's rage Freeze thy blood less cold - - - ly.'

14. HARK! THE HERALD ANGELS SING

Words by C. WESLEY,
T. WHITEFIELD, M. MADAN
and others

MENDELSSOHN
Descant and organ part by
DAVID WILLCOCKS

Melody, and harmony for vv. 1 and 2, adapted by W. H. Cummings (1831-1915) from a chorus by Mendelssohn.
Verses 1 and 2 may be sung by unison voices and organ if desired. *Deity* pronounced *Dee-ity*

15. IN DULCI JUBILO

Edited and adapted by REGINALD JACQUES

Old German tune
arranged by R.L. PEARSALL

The original melody employed, as a *Cantus firmus*, in the following composition, is to be found in an old German book published in the year 1570,—which, from its title and contents, appears to have contained the ritual of the Protestant Congregations of Zweibrueken and Neuburg. Even there it is called " a very ancient song *(uraltes Lied)* for Christmas-eve;" so that there can be no doubt that it is one of those old Roman Catholic melodies that Luther, on account of their beauty, retained in the Protestant Service. It was formerly sung in the processions that took place on Christmas-eve, and is so still in those remote parts of Germany where people yet retain old customs. The words are rather remarkable, being written half in Latin and half in the upper German dialect. I have translated them to fit the music, and endeavoured to preserve, as much as I could, the simplicity of the original. Of the melody there can be but one opinion; namely, that which in spite of religious animosity, secured it the approbation of the Protestant reformers, and that of the German people during many centuries. The music in the following passages was written for the Choral Society at Carlsruhe, and was performed there in the Autumn of 1834.
Willsbridge, Gloucestershire, 31st of January, 1837. R.L.P.

VERSE 1 : CHOIR I
VERSE 2 : CHOIR II

EDITOR'S NOTE

Pearsall wrote the following footnote in his original : 'The time of this melody should not be taken very slow. It must be borne in mind that the Semibreve and Minim were two of the shortest notes employed by Ancient Composers.'
Pearsall's translation of the second line of verse 2 was 'My heart is sore for thee!'
The expression marks are Pearsall's.

CHOIRS I and II

D.C. for Verse 2

shi - neth, Ma - tris in gre - mi - o. _____
reach thee, O Prin - ceps glo - ri - æ! _____

Al - pha es et O, _____ Al - pha es et O.
Tra - he me post te! _____ tra - he me post te!

D.C. for Verse 2

*or a few voices

*or a few voices

bells___ are ring - ing In Re - gis cu - ri - a:

-ing In Re - - - gis cu - ri - a: *FULL f*   O___ that we were

In   Re - gis cu - ri - a: *FULL f*   O that we were

ring - - - ing In Re - gis cu - - ri - a: *FULL f*   O that

bells are ring - ing In Re - gis cu - ri - a: *FULL f*   O that we were there,

In Re - gis cu - ri - a: *FULL f*   O___ that we were

bells___   are ring - ing In cu - ri - a: *FULL f*   O that we were

ring - ing there In Re - gis cu - ri - a: *FULL f*   O that

16. INFANT HOLY, INFANT LOWLY

Tr. EDITH M. REED

Polish carol
arranged by DAVID WILLCOCKS

Words reprinted by permission of Evans Brothers Ltd.

17. I SAW THREE SHIPS

(First tune)

English traditional carol
arranged by DAVID WILLCOCKS

1. I saw three ships come sail-ing in, I
3. Our Sa-viour Christ and his la-dy, *On Christ-mas Day, on Christ-mas Day,* Our
5. O, they sailed in - to Beth-le-hem, O,

On Christ-mas Day, on Christ - mas__

saw three ships come sail - ing in,
Sa - viour Christ and his la - dy, *On Christ-mas Day in the morn - ing.*
they sailed in - to Beth - le - hem,

Day,

2. And what was in those ships all three? And
4. Pray, whi-ther sailed those ships all three? *On Christ-mas Day, on Christ-mas Day,* Pray,

On Christ-mas Day, on Christ - mas__

what was in those ships all three? *On Christ - mas Day in the morn - ing.*
whi - ther sailed those ships all three?

Day,

D.C. for vv. 3 & 5

Note: Dynamics are left to the discretion of the conductor.

© 1960 Oxford University Press

17. I SAW THREE SHIPS

(Second tune)

Words traditional   REGINALD JACQUES

SOPRANOS
mf

Christ - mas Day in the morn - ing. 2. And what was in those
5. O, they sailed in - to
8. And all the souls on

ALL SOPRANOS

ships all three? And
Beth - le - hem, *On Christ - mas Day,* *on Christ - mas Day,* O,
earth shall sing, And

ALL

what was in those ships all three?
they sailed in - to Beth - le - hem, *On Christ - mas Day in the*
all the souls on earth shall sing,

SOPRANOS

3. Our Sa - viour Christ and his la - dy,
morn - ing. 6. And all the bells on earth shall ring, On
9. Then let us all re - joice a - main!

SOPRANOS

Christ - mas Day, on Christ - mas Day, Our Sa - viour Christ and
And all the bells on
Then let us all re -

ALL   D.C.

his la - dy, On Christ - mas Day in the morn - ing.
earth shall ring,
- joice a - main!

(Last time only)

(Last time only)

18. IT CAME UPON THE MIDNIGHT CLEAR

Words by
E.H. SEARS

Traditional English tune
adapted by ARTHUR SULLIVAN

In moderate time ♩ = 92

SOPRANO
ALTO

1. It— came up - on the— mid-night clear, That glo-rious song of old,
2. Still through the clo - ven— skies they come, With peace-ful wings un-furled;

TENOR
BASS

From an - gels bend-ing near the earth To— touch their harps of gold:
And still their heav'n-ly mu - sic floats O'er— all— the wea - ry world;

'Peace on the earth, good-will to men, From heav'n's all - grac - ious King!'
A - bove its sad and low - ly plains They bend on ho - v'ring wing;

The world in so - lemn still-ness lay To— hear the an-gels sing.
And e - ver o'er its— Ba - bel sounds The bless-ed an-gels sing.

3. Yet with the woes of sin and strife
   The world has suffered long;
   Beneath the angel-strain have rolled
   Two thousand years of wrong;
   And man, at war with man, hears not
   The love-song which they bring:
   O hush the noise, ye men of strife,
   And hear the angels sing!

4. For lo! the days are hastening on,
   By prophet-bards foretold,
   When, with the ever-circling years,
   Comes round the age of gold;
   When peace shall over all the earth
   Its ancient splendours fling,
   And the whole world send back the song
   Which now the angels sing.

To Geoffrey Shaw

19. A MERRY CHRISTMAS

Traditional (West country) carol
arranged by ARTHUR WARRELL

pud - ding, Now bring us some fig-gy pud - ding, And bring some out

bring us some fig-gy pud - ding, Now bring us fig-gy pud - ding, out

Good tid - ings I bring____ To_ you and your
(We)

Good tid - ings I bring To you and your kin; I
(We) (We)

here. Good tid - ings I bring_ To you_ and your kin; I
(We) (We)

here. Good tid - ings I bring To you and your kin; I
(We) (We)

20. KING JESUS HATH A GARDEN

Tr. G.R. WOODWARD

Dutch tune
harmonized by CHARLES WOOD

1. King Je - sus hath a gar-den, full of di - vers flow'rs, Where
2. The Li - ly, white in blos-som there, is Chas - ti - ty: The

I go cull - ing po - sies gay, all times_ and_ hours. *There*
Vi - o - let, with sweet per - fume, Hu - mi - li - ty.

naught is heard but Pa - ra - dise bird, Harp, dul - ci - mer, lute, With

cym - bal, _ trump and tym - bal, And the ten - der,_ sooth - ing flute; With

Reprinted from *The Cowley Carol Book* by permission

cym - bal,___ trump and tym-bal, And the ten - der,_ sooth-ing flute.___

3. The bonny Damask-rose is known as Patïence:
    The blithe and thrifty Marygold, Obedïence.

    There naught is heard, etc.

4. The Crown Imperial bloometh too in yonder place,
    'Tis Charity, of stock divine, the flower of grace.

    There naught is heard, etc.

5. Yet, 'mid the brave, the bravest prize of all may claim⌣
    The Star of Bethlem — Jesus — blessèd be his Name!

    There naught is heard, etc.

6. Ah! Jesu Lord, my heal and weal, my bliss complete,
    Make thou my heart thy garden-plot, fair, trim and neat.
    That I may hear this musick clear:
    Harp, dulcimer, lute,
    With cymbal, trump and tymbal,
    And the tender, soothing flute.

21. ROCKING

Tr. PERCY DEARMER

Czech carol
arranged by DAVID WILLCOCKS

1. Lit-tle Je-sus, sweet-ly sleep, do not stir;
2. Ma-ry's lit-tle ba-by, sleep, sweet-ly sleep,

We will lend a coat of fur,
Sleep in com-fort, slum-ber deep;
We will rock you,

Words and melody from *The Oxford Book of Carols*, by permission

© 1960 Oxford University Press

22. CAROL, WITH LULLABY

Words anon.
(adapted by PHYLLIS TATE)

PHYLLIS TATE

reign, ___ shalt live and reign, ___ As all the pro-phets

reign ___ who was in ___ a man-ger laid, ___ As all the pro-phets

reign who was in a man-ger laid, ___ As all ___ the pro-phets

reign, ___ shalt live and reign, ___ As all ___ the pro-phets

pro-phe-sy, as sy-bils have fore-said; ___ Whom cai-tiffs ne'er be-

pro-phe-sy, as sy-bils have fore-said; ___ Whom cai-tiffs ne'er be-

pro-phe-sy, as sy-bils have fore-said; ___ Whom cai-tiffs ne'er be-

pro-phe-sy, as sy-bils have fore-said; ___ Whom cai-tiffs ne'er be-

23. COVENTRY CAROL

(First version)

Pageant of the Shearmen and Tailors, 15th century

Original tune of 1591

The above Refrain and First Verse is scored from the original.

2. Herod, the king,
   In his raging,
   Chargèd he hath this day
   His men of might,
   In his own sight,
   All young childrèn to slay.

3. That woe is me,
   Poor child for thee!
   And ever morn and day,
   For thy parting
   Neither say nor sing
   By by, lully lullay!

This song is sung by the women of Bethlehem in the play, just before Herod's soldiers come in to slaughter their children.

*The original manuscript has F and D in tenor part here.

23. COVENTRY CAROL
(Second version)

Modern version of tune
arranged by MARTIN SHAW

This song is sung by the women of Bethlehem in the play, just before Herod's soldiers come in to slaughter their children.

The arrangement of the second version is reprinted by permission of A. R. Mowbray & Co. Ltd.

24. NO SAD THOUGHT HIS SOUL AFFRIGHT

Words:
Verse 1. Anon.
Verse 2. URSULA VAUGHAN WILLIAMS*

R. VAUGHAN WILLIAMS

*By permission

Reprinted from the cantata *Hodie* (O.U.P.)

© 1954 Oxford University Press

† pronounce 'wind' to rhyme with 'kind'

25. O LITTLE ONE SWEET

Tr. PERCY DEARMER

Old German tune
harmonized by J. S. BACH

3. O little one sweet, O little one mild,
   In thee Love's beauties are all distilled;
     Then light in us thy love's bright flame,
     That we may give thee back the same,
   O little one sweet, O little one mild.

4. O little one sweet, O little one mild,
   Help us to do as thou hast willed.
     Lo, all we have belongs to thee!
     Ah, keep us in our fealty!
   O little one sweet, O little one mild.

Reprinted from *The Oxford Book of Carols* by permission

26. O COME, ALL YE FAITHFUL

(ADESTE FIDELES)

Tr. F. OAKELEY, W. T. BROOKE
and others

Composer unknown (probably 18th c.)
arranged by DAVID WILLCOCKS

1. O come, all ye faith - ful, Joy - ful and tri -
2. God of God, Light of

-um - phant, O come ye, O come ye to Beth - le - hem;
Light, Lo! he ab - hors not the Vir - gin's womb;

Come and be - hold him Born the King of An - gels: O
Ve - ry God, Be - got - ten, not cre - a - ted: O

come, let us a - dore him, O come, let us a - dore him, O

come, let us a - dore him, Christ the Lord!

Man.

Ped.

Note: Verses 1-5 may be sung by unison voices and organ, S.A.T.B. voices and organ, or voices unaccompanied as desired. Verses 3-5 may be omitted. The harmonies used for vv. 1-5 are from *The English Hymnal*.

3. See how the shepherds,
    Summoned to his cradle,
    Leaving their flocks, draw nigh with lowly fear;
    We too will thither
    Bend our joyful footsteps :
            O come, etc.

4. Lo! star-led chieftains,
    Magi, Christ adoring,
    Offer him incense, gold and myrrh;
    We to the Christ Child
    Bring our hearts' oblations :
            O come, etc.

5. Child, for us sinners
    Poor and in the manger,
    Fain we embrace thee, with awe and love;
    Who would not love thee,
    Loving us so dearly?
            O come, etc.

All voices

7. Yea, Lord, we greet thee, Born this hap-py morn - ing, Je - su, to

thee be glo - ry giv'n; Word of the Fa - ther,

Now in flesh ap-pear - ing: O come, let us a - dore him, O come, let us a-

-dore him, O come, let us a - dore him, Christ the Lord!

27. O LITTLE TOWN OF BETHLEHEM

Words by BISHOP PHILLIPS BROOKS

English traditional tune
arranged by R. VAUGHAN WILLIAMS.
Descant by THOMAS ARMSTRONG

1. O lit-tle town of_ Beth-le-hem, How still we_ see thee lie!
2. O morn-ing stars, to-geth-er_ Pro-claim the_ ho-ly birth,
3. How si-lent-ly, how si-lent-ly, The won-drous gift is giv'n!

A-bove thy deep and_ dream-less sleep The si-lent stars go by.
And prais-es sing to_ God the King, And peace to men on earth;
So God im-parts to_ hu-man hearts The bless-ings of his heav'n.

Yet in thy dark streets shin-eth The ev-er-last-ing_ light;
For Christ is born of Ma-ry; And, gath-ered all a-bove,
No ear may hear his com-ing; But in this world of_ sin,

The hopes and fears of_ all_ the_ years Are met in_ thee to-night.
While mor-tals sleep, the_ an-gels_ keep Their watch of_ wond-'ring love.
Where meek souls will re-ceive him, still_ The dear Christ en-ters in.

Descant reprinted by permission of The Royal School of Church Music

DESCANT

4. O ho - ly__Child of Beth-le - hem, Des - cend to us, we pray;

ORGAN or PIANO

UNISON VOICES

Cast out our__ sin, and en - ter in, Be born in us to - day.

We__ hear the Christ-mas an - gels The great glad ti - dings tell:

O come to__ us, a - bide with us, Our Lord Em-man-u - el.

28. O MEN FROM THE FIELDS

A CRADLE SONG

(Solo or unison voices)

Words by
PADRAIC COLUM

ARNOLD COOKE

O men from the fields! Come gen-tly with-in. Tread soft-ly, soft-ly, O men com-ing in! Ma-vour-neen is go-ing From me and from you, Where Ma-ry will fold him With man-tle of blue!

Words reprinted by permission

(Solo)
From reek of the smoke, And cold of the floor, And the peer-ing of things A - cross the half-door.

(Unison)
O men from the fields! Soft, soft - ly come through— Ma - ry puts round him Her man - tle of blue.

Homage to R.V.W.

29. SUSSEX CAROL

English traditional carol
arranged by DAVID WILLCOCKS

Melody and words reprinted by permission of Ursula Vaughan Williams

© 1961 Oxford University Press

1st time (v.1)
SOPRANOS (and ALTOS)

News of great joy,— news of— great mirth,

FULL

News of our mer - ci - ful— King's birth.

2nd time (v.2)
(Voices unaccompanied)
S.
A.

When from our sin— he set— us free,—

T.

B. (Organ tacet)

All for to gain our lib - er - ty?

ORGAN

3. When sin de-parts be-fore his grace, Then life and health come

1st time *mf* Ah
2nd time *p*

(Voices unaccompanied)

in its place; When in its place; An - gels and men with joy may

An - gels and men with

sing, All for to see the new-born King.

joy may sing, All for to see the new-born King.

30. ONCE IN ROYAL DAVID'S CITY

Words by C.F. ALEXANDER

H.J. GAUNTLETT
harmonized by A.H. MANN

1. Once in roy-al Da-vid's_ ci-ty Stood a low-ly cat-tle_ shed,
Where a mo-ther laid_her_ ba-by In a man-ger for_ his_ bed:

2. He came down to earth from hea-ven Who is God and Lord of_ all,
And his shel-ter was_ a_ sta-ble, And his cra-dle was_ a_ stall;

Ma - ry_ was that mo-ther mild,_ Je - sus_ Christ_ her lit - tle child._
With the_ poor and mean and low-ly Lived on_ earth_our Sa-viour ho - ly.

3. And through all his wondrous childhood
   He would honour and obey,
   Love and watch the lowly maiden,
   In whose gentle arms he lay:
   Christian children all must be
   Mild, obedient, good as he.

4. For he is our childhood's pattern,
   Day by day like us he grew,
   He was little, weak, and helpless,
   Tears and smiles like us he knew:
   And he feeleth for our sadness,
   And he shareth in our gladness.

5. And our eyes at last shall see him,
   Through his own redeeming love,
   For that child so dear and gentle
   Is our Lord in heaven above;
   And he leads his children on
   To the place where he is gone.

6. Not in that poor lowly stable,
   With the oxen standing by,
   We shall see him; but in heaven,
   Set at God's right hand on high;
   Where like stars his children crowned
   All in white shall wait around.

31. PAST THREE A CLOCK

Words by
G. R. WOODWARD

Traditional carol
harmonized by CHARLES WOOD

SOPRANO
ALTO

Past three a clock, And a cold fro-sty morn - ing: Past three a clock; Good

TENOR
BASS

Fine

mor-row, mas-ters all!

1. Born is a ba - by, Gen - tle as may be,
2. Se - raph quire sing - eth, An - gel bell ring - eth:

Son — of — th' e - ter - nal Fa - ther su - per - nal,
Hark — how — they rime — it, Time it, and chime it.

Past three a clock,

3. Mid earth rejoices
   Hearing such voices
   Ne'ertofore só well
   Carolling *Nowell.*
   Past three a clock, etc.

4. Hinds o'er the pearly
   Dewy lawn early
   Seek the high stranger
   Laid in the manger.
   Past three a clock, etc.

5. Cheese from the dairy
   Bring they for Mary,
   And, not for money,
   Butter and honey.
   Past three a clock, etc.

6. Light out of star-land
   Leadeth from far land
   Princes, to meet him,
   Worship and greet him.
   Past three a clock, etc.

7. Myrrh from full coffer,
   Incense they offer:
   Nor is the golden
   Nugget withholden.
   Past three a clock, etc.

8. Thus they: I pray you,
   Up, sirs, nor stay you
   Till ye confess him
   Likewise, and bless him.
   Past three a clock, etc.

The refrain *Past three a clock* is old, but the other words are by G. R. W. The tune is *London Waits,* from W. Chappell's *Popular Music of the Olden Time.*

Reprinted from *The Cambridge Carol Book* by permission

32. REJOICE AND BE MERRY

(A GALLERY CAROL)

English traditional carol
arranged by REGINALD JACQUES

1. Re - joice and be mer - ry in songs and in mirth!' O
2. A hea - ven - ly vi - sion ap - peared in the sky; Vast

praise our Re-deem-er, all mor-tals on earth! For this is the birth-day of
num - bers of an- gels the shep-herds did spy, Pro - claim- ing the birth-day of

Je - sus our King, Who brought us sal - va - tion—his prai - ses we'll sing!
Je - sus our King, Who brought us sal - va - tion—his prai - ses we'll sing!

3. Likewise a bright star in the sky did appear,
   Which led the wise men from the east to draw near;
   They found the Messiah, sweet Jesus our King,
   Who brought us salvation—his praises we'll sing!

4. And when they were come, they their treasures unfold,
   And unto him offered myrrh, incense, and gold.
   So blessèd for ever be Jesus our King,
   Who brought us salvation—his praises we'll sing!

33. SEE AMID THE WINTER'S SNOW

Words by E. CASWALL

JOHN GOSS
arranged by DAVID WILLCOCKS

1. See a-mid the win-ter's snow, Born for us on earth be-low; See the ten-der Lamb ap-pears, Pro-mis'd from e-ter-nal years:

Hail, thou e-ver-bless-ed morn; Hail, re-demp-tion's hap-py dawn; Sing through all Je-ru-sa-lem,— Christ is born in Beth-le-hem.

The harmonizations used for the refrain in verses 1, 3, and 4 are Goss's own.

© 1961 Oxford University Press

after verse 5 to page 106 for last verse

TENORS
I & II

4. 'As we watch'd at dead of night, Lo, we saw a won-drous light;

4. 'As we watch'd at dead of night, Lo, we saw a won-drous

BASSES

4. 'As we watch'd at dead of night, Lo, we saw a wondrous light; An-gels sing-ing

mf An-gels sing-ing, Told us of the Sa-viour's birth:'

light;— An-gels sing-ing of the Sa-viour's birth:'

CHORUS

S. *f* Hail, thou e-ver-bless-ed morn;

A.

T.

"Peace on earth" Told us of the Sa-viour's birth:'

B. *f* (organ *ad lib.*)

to 𝄋 (p. 104)
for verse 5

Hail, re-demp-tion's hap-py dawn; Sing through all Je-ru-sa-lem, Christ is born in Beth-le-hem.

ALL VOICES

f

6. Teach, O teach us, Ho-ly Child, By thy face so

ORGAN

Man.   Ped.

meek and mild, Teach us to re-sem-ble thee, In thy sweet hu-mi-li-ty:

CHOIR I
(and audience)

Hail, thou e - ver - bless-ed morn; Hail, re-demp-tion's hap-py dawn;

CHOIR II

Hail, thou e - ver - bless-ed morn; Hail, re-demp-tion's hap-py dawn;

ORGAN

Largamente

Sing through all Je - ru - sa-lem, Christ is born in Beth - le - hem.

Largamente

Sing through all Je - ru - sa-lem, — Christ is — born in Beth - le - hem.

Largamente

34. LUTE-BOOK LULLABY

Words by
W. BALLET

W. BALLET (17th c.)
arranged by GEOFFREY SHAW

lul - la, lul - la - by. 2. 'Sweet babe,'___ sang___ she, 'my

son, And eke a — sa - viour born, Who hast vouch-

-saf - ed from on high To vis - it us that were for-

To vis - it us,___ us that were for-

-lorn: La-lu - la, la - lu - la, la - lu - la - by. Sweet babe,' sang

-lorn: La-lu - la, la - lu - la, la - lu - la - by. Sweet babe,' sang

she, And rocked him sweet - - - ly___ on her knee.

From the MS. *Lute Book* by William Ballet, early seventeenth century, Trinity College, Dublin.

35. THE LINDEN TREE CAROL

Tr. G. R. WOODWARD

Old German tune
arranged by REGINALD JACQUES

1. There stood in heav'n a lin - den tree, But, tho' t'was ho - ney la - - den, All an - gels cried, 'No bloom shall be Like that of one fair maid - en.'

3. 'Hail Ma - ry!' quoth the an - gel mild, 'Of wo - man - kind the fair - est: The Vir - gin ay shalt thou be styled, A babe al - though thou bear - est.'

5. This ti - ding fill'd his mates with glee: 'Twas pass'd from one to o - ther, That 'twas Ma - ry, and none but she, And God would call her Mo - ther.

Words reprinted from *The Cambridge Carol Book* by permission

© 1961 Oxford University Press

SOPRANO
ALTO

Verses 2, 4

2. Sped_ Ga - bri - el   on   wing - - ed
4. 'So__ be   it!' God's   hand - maid - - en

TENOR
and
BARITONE

feet,   And   pass'd__ through bolt - ed   por - - -
cried, 'Ac - cord - ing   to __   thy   tell - - -

-tals   In   Na - za - reth,__ a   maid__ to
-ing.' Where - on__ the   an - gel   smart - ly

(D.C. vv. 3&5)

greet,__ Blest o'er__ all   o - ther mor - - tals.
hied__ Up   home - ward to__ his   dwell - - ing.

36. THE BLESSED SON OF GOD

Words by
MILES COVERDALE
after MARTIN LUTHER

R. VAUGHAN WILLIAMS

The bless-ed son of God on-ly In a crib full poor did lie; With our poor flesh and our poor blood Was clothed that ev-er-

Reprinted from the cantata *Hodie* (O.U.P.)

-last - ing good. {Ky - ri - e - lei - - son. / Lord have mer - - cy. The

-last - ing good. {Ky - ri - e - lei - - son. / Lord have mer - - cy. The

-last - ing good. {Ky - ri - e - lei - - son. / Lord have mer - - cy. The

-last - ing good. {Ky - ri - e - lei - - son. / Lord have mer - - cy. The

Lord Christ Je - su, God's son— dear, Was a guest and a strang - er here;

Lord Christ Je - su, God's son— dear, Was a guest and a strang - er here;

Lord Christ Je - su, God's son— dear, Was a guest and a strang - er here;

Lord Christ Je - su, God's son— dear, Was a guest and a strang - er here;

for us free-ly, For to de-clare his great mer - cy; All Christ-en-dom be mer-ry there-fore, And give him thanks for ev - er-more,

for us free-ly, For to de-clare his great mer - cy;— All Christ-en-dom— be mer-ry there-fore, And give him thanks for ev - er - more,—

for us free-ly, For to de-clare his great mer - cy;— All Christ-en-dom be mer-ry there-fore, And give him thanks for ev - er - more,—

us free - ly, For to de-clare his great mer - cy; All Christ-en-dom be mer-ry there-fore, And give him thanks for ev - er-more,

To Cuthbert Bates and the City of Bath Bach Choir,
by whom this setting was commissioned.

37. THE BOAR'S HEAD CAROL

English traditional carol
arranged by ELIZABETH POSTON

Liberamente, marcato impetuoso

SOPRANO

Now-ell, now-ell, now-ell, now-ell, Now-ell, now-ell, ___ now-ell,

ALTO

Now-ell, now-ell, now-ell, now-ell, Now-ell, now-ell, ___ now-ell,

TENOR

Now-ell, now-ell, now-ell, now-ell, ___

BASS

Now-ell, now-ell, now-ell, now-ell, ___

(for practice only)

Con spirito

now-ell. ___ Now - - - - - ell. ___

now-ell. ___ Now - - - - - ell. ___

Tid-ings good I think to tell. ___

Tid-ings good I think to tell. ___ 1. The

poco ritenuto ___ a tempo

meno f

The tune, and the words of verses 1, 2, and 5, are as sung at Queen's College, Oxford. To provide an optional extension of the Oxford carol, two verses have been incorporated (nos. 3 & 4), fitted to the Oxford tune, from a Boar's Head carol of BM MS Addit. 5665, c. 1500, bearing the signature Smert, and probably from the West Country, where Richard Smert was rector of Plymtree near Exeter, 1435-1477.

(Bass Solo)

boar's head in hand bear I,   Be-deck'd with bays and rose - ma - ry.   And I

pray you, my mas-ters,   be mer - ry,   Quot es - tis   in   con - vi - vi - o.

Ca - put   a - pri   de - fe - ro,   Red - dens lau - des Do - mi - no.

2. The boar's   head, as I un - der - stand, Is the brav-est dish in all   the

land, When thus be-deck'd with a gay gar - land. Let us ser - vi - re can - ti - co.

*Alternative in small notes in case it be found preferable to reserve high tenor tone
for later passages. Altos divide (small notes) if tenors use alternative notes.

Ca - put a - pri_ de - fe - ro,__ Red-dens lau - des__ Do - mi - no.

Ca - put a - pri de - fe - ro, Red - dens lau - des Do - mi - no.

OPTIONAL SEMI-CHORUS

(Now-ell, now-ell, now - ell, now - ell,__ now - ell,__ now - ell, now-

3. The boar's head that we bring here Be - to-ken-eth a prince with-out - e

(Now-ell, now-ell, now-ell, now - ell,__ now - ell,__ now - ell, now-

Now - ell, now-ell, now - ell, now - ell,__ now - ell,__ now-ell, now-

FULL

Ca - put a - pri de - fe - ro, Red - dens lau - des Do - mi - no.

Ca - put a - pri de - fe - ro, Red - dens lau - des Do - mi - no.

Ca - put a - pri de - fe - ro, Red - dens lau - des Do - mi - no.

Ca - put a - pri de - fe - ro, Red - dens lau - des Do - mi - no.

OPTIONAL SEMI-CHORUS

Now - - ell, now - ell, _____

4. This boar's head we bring with song, _____ Now - ell, _____

4. This boar's head we bring with song, _____

Now - ell, _____ In wor - ship

Ca - put a - pri de - fe - ro, —— Red - dens lau - des—
Ca - put a - pri de - fe - ro, Red - dens lau - des
Ca - put a - pri de - fe - ro, Red - dens lau - des
Ca - put a - pri de - fe - ro, Red - dens lau - des

Largamente

Do - mi - no.   -no. Now - ell,   now - ell.
Do - mi - no.   -no. Now - ell,   now - ell.
Do - mi - no.   -no. Now - ell, —— now - ell.
Do - mi - no.   -no. Now - ell, —— now - ell.

38. THE FIRST NOWELL

English traditional carol
arranged by DAVID WILLCOCKS

VOICES

ORGAN

The first No-well the an-gel did say Was to cer-tain poor shep-herds in fields as they lay; In fields where they lay, keep-ing their sheep, On a cold win-ter's night that was so deep: No-well, No-well, No-well, No-well, Born is the King of Is-ra-el!

SOPRANO
ALTO

(ORGAN)

2. They look - ed _ up __ and _ saw __ a _ star, __ Shining
4. This star __ drew nigh __ to __ the __ north-west; __ O'er _

TENOR
BASS

in __ the east, __ be - yond _ them far; __ And to __ the earth _ it
Beth - le - hem _ it took __ its rest, __ And there _ it did __ both

gave _ great light, __ And so it con - tin - ued both day __ and night:
stop __ and stay __ Right ov - er the _ place _ where Je - sus lay:

REFRAIN (voices in unison)

No - well, __ No - well, No - well, No - well,

ORGAN

Born is the King __ of Is - ra - el!

Note : vv. 2 & 4 may be sung by unaccompanied voices.

SOPRANO
ALTO

(ORGAN)

mp 3. And by the light of that same star, Three
pp 5. Then en - ter'd in those wise men three, Full

MELODY *(mf)*

TENOR
BASS

wise men came from coun - try far; To seek for a king was
re - v'rent -ly up - on their knee, And off - er'd there in

their in - tent, And to fol - low the star wher - ev - er it went:
his pre - sence Their gold and myrrh and frank - in - cense:

REFRAIN

No - well, No - well, No - well, No - well,

Dal 𝄋 for v. 4
(page 127)

Born is the King of Is - ra - el!

Note: vv. 3 & 5 may be sung unaccompanied, or with organ, or by unison voices (tenor part) with descant
(soprano part), and organ.

VOICES

6. Then let— us— all with— one— ac - cord Sing prai - ses

ORGAN

to— our heav'n - ly Lord, That hath— made heav'n and— earth— of

REFRAIN
DESCANT (Sops.)

naught, And with— his blood— man - kind— hath bought: *No - well,— No-*

-well, No - well, No - well,   Born is the King— of Is - ra - el!

To the Bach Choir

39. THE HOLLY AND THE IVY

English traditional carol
arranged by REGINALD JACQUES

Reprinted by permission of Novello & Co. Ltd. This carol was collected by Cecil Sharp.

2. The hol-ly bears a blos-som, As white as the li-ly flower; And

2. The hol-ly bears a blos-som,— As white as the li-ly flower; And

Ma-ry bore sweet Je-sus Christ, To— be our sweet Sa-viour.— The

Ma-ry bore sweet Je-sus Christ, To— be our sweet Sa-viour.— The

The

The

3. The hol-ly bears a ber-ry, As red as a-ny blood; And

3. The hol-ly bears a ber-ry, As red as a-ny blood; And

And

And

Ma-ry bore sweet Je-sus Christ, For to do us sin-ners good. The

Ma-ry bore sweet Je-sus Christ, For to do us sin-ners good. The

Ma-ry bore sweet Je-sus Christ, For to do us sin-ners good. The

Ma-ry bore sweet Je-sus Christ, For to do us sin-ners good. The

5. The hol-ly bears a bark,— As bit-ter as a-ny gall; And—

5. The hol-ly bears a bark,— As bit-ter as a-ny gall; And

as a-ny gall;— And—

Ma-ry bore sweet Je-sus Christ, For— to re-deem us all. The

Ma-ry bore sweet Je-sus Christ, For— to re-deem us all.— The

Ma-ry bore sweet Je-sus Christ, For to re-deem us all. The

Ma-ry bore sweet Je-sus Christ, For to re-deem us all.— The

After verse 5 repeat verse 1

40. THE THREE KINGS

Tr. H. N. BATE

PETER CORNELIUS
arranged by IVOR ATKINS

SOLO

1. Three kings from Per - sian lands a - far To Jor-dan fol - low the point - ing star: And this the quest of the tra - vel-lers three, Where the morn - ing star!

SOPRANO

ALTO

TENOR

* CHORALE Wie schön leuchtet der Morgenstern
pp well sustained

How bright-ly shines the morn - ing star! With grace and

BASS

pp well sustained

How bright-ly shines the morn - ing star! With grace and

(for practice only)

* The singers should be placed, if possible, at some distance from the soloist.

© 1930 Oxford University Press, London. Renewed in U.S.A. 1958 new-born King of the Jews may— be. Full roy-al gifts they bear for the

truth from heav'n a - far Our

truth from heav'n a - far Our

King; Gold, in-cense, myrrh are their of-fer-ing. 2. The star shines

Jes - se tree— now blow - - eth.

Jes - se tree now blow - - eth.

lo, to Beth-le-hem   The kings are trav - lling,— trav-el with them!

_____   Je - su, _____

Thy   word,   Je - su,   Je - su,

Thy___ word,   Je - su, _____   Je - su,

Thy   word,   Je - su,   Je - su,

poco a poco più mosso

The star of mer - cy, the star of grace, Shall lead thy_heart to its rest ▸ ing -

poco a poco più mosso

In - ly   feeds   us,   Right - ly   leads   us,

poco a poco più mosso

In - ly   feeds   us,___ Right - ly   leads   us,___

poco a poco piu mosso

In - ly   feeds   us,___ Right - ly   leads   us,___

In - ly   feeds   us,   Right - ly   leads   us,

poco a poco più mosso

41. THE SHEPHERDS' FAREWELL

(FROM 'L'ENFANCE DU CHRIST' Op.25)

Words by PAUL ENGLAND

HECTOR BERLIOZ

* Here, and elsewhere, alternative notes (small) are provided for basses.

Words reprinted by permission of Novello & Co. Ltd.

42. TORCHES

Tr. J. B. TREND
(from the Galician)

JOHN JOUBERT

1. Tor-ches, tor-ches, run with tor-ches All the way to Beth-le-hem! Christ is born and now lies sleep-ing; Come and sing your song to him! Tor-ches, tor-ches, run with tor-ches All the way to Beth-le-hem! Christ is born and now lies sleep-ing; Come and sing your song to him!

Words from *The Oxford Book of Carols* by permission
Music reprinted by permission of Novello & Co. Ltd.

SOPRANO Ah, Ro - ro, Ro - ro,— my— ba- by, Ah,— Ro - ro, my— love, Ro - ro;

ALTO Ro - ro,———— Ro - ro,————

TENOR Ro - ro,———— Ro - ro,————

BASS Ro - ro,———— Ro - ro,————

p unaccompanied ad lib.

Man.

Sleep you well, my heart's own— dar - ling, While we— sing you— our Ro - ro.

Ro - ro,———— Ro - ro, sing Ro - ro.

Ro - ro,———— Ro - ro, sing Ro - ro.

Ro - ro,———— Ro - ro, sing Ro - ro.

Sing, my friends, and make you mer-ry, Joy and mirth and

Sing, my friends, and make you mer-ry,

Sing, my friends, and make you mer-ry, Joy and mirth and

Sing, my friends, and make you mer-ry,

Ped.

joy a-gain; Lo, he lives, the King of hea-ven, Now and ev-er-

Sing, my friends, and make you mer-ry, Sing my friends, Now and ev-er-

joy a-gain; Lo, he lives, the King of hea-ven, Now and ev-er-

Sing, my friends, and make you mer-ry, Sing, my friends, Now and ev-er-

43. UNTO US IS BORN A SON

Tr. G. R. WOODWARD

Tune from *Piae Cantiones*, 1582
arranged by DAVID WILLCOCKS

1. Un-to us is born a Son, King of quires su - per - nal: See on earth his life be-gun, Of lords the Lord e - ter - nal, of lords the Lord' e - ter - nal.

2. Christ, from heav'n des-cend-ing low, Comes on earth a stran - ger; Ox and ass their

*Voices unaccompanied

*may be sung accompanied, or by unison voices and organ
Words reprinted from *The Cowley Carol Book* by permission

own-er know, Be-cra-dled in the_ man-ger, be-cra-dled in the man-ger.

TENORS and BASSES

3. This did He-rod sore af-fray, And grie-vous-ly be-wild-er, So he gave the

Full Sw.

Ped. Man.

word to slay, And slew the lit-tle chil-der, and slew the lit-tle chil-der.

Ped.

SOPRANOS

4. Of his love and mer-cy mild This the Christ-mas sto-ry; And O that Ma-ry's

Man.

gen-tle Child Might lead us up to glo-ry, might lead us up to glo-ry!

Ist Choir

UNISON
VOICES

5. O and A, and A and O, *Cum cant-i-bus in cho - ro,*   Let our mer-ry

Coom.

*2nd Choir

SOPRANO
ALTO

TENOR
BASS

5. O and A, and A and O, *Cum cant-i-bus in cho - ro,*   Let our mer-ry

ORGAN

Man.   Ped.

or - gan go, *Be - ne-di-ca-mus Do-mi-no, be - ne - di - ca-mus Do - mi-no.*

or - gan go, *Be - ne - di - ca-mus Do-mi-no, be - ne - di - ca-mus Do-mi - no.*

*optional, or soprano part as a descant.

44. UP! GOOD CHRISTEN FOLK, AND LISTEN

Words by
G.R. WOODWARD

Tune from *Piae Cantiones*, 1582
harmonized by G.R. WOODWARD

Ding-dong, ding: Ding-a-dong-a-ding: Ding-dong, ding-dong: Ding-a-dong-ding.

Up! good Christen folk, and list-en—How the mer-ry church——bells ring,
Tell the sto-ry how from glo-ry—God came down at Christ——mas-tide,

And from stee-ple—bid good peo-ple Come a-dore the new—born—King:
Bring-ing glad-ness,—cha-sing sad-ness, Show'ring blessings far———and—wide,

Born of—mo-ther, blest o'er o-ther, *Ex Ma-ri-a Vir-gi-ne,*

In a sta-ble ('tis no fa-ble), *Chris-tus na-tus ho-di-e.*

Reprinted from *The Cowley Carol Book* by permission

45. WE'VE BEEN AWHILE A-WANDERING

Traditional Yorkshire carol
collected and arranged by
R. VAUGHAN WILLIAMS

The accompaniment may be performed
by voices ('Ah' or humming)

1. We've been a-while a-wan-der-ing A-
2. We are not dai - ly beg - gars That

-mongst the leaves so green,— But now we come a - was - sail-ing, So
beg from door to door;— We are your neigh - bours' child - ren, For

plain - ly to be seen; *For it's Christmas time, when we tra-vel far and near; May God*
we've been here be - fore;

bless you and send you a hap-py New Year.

3. We've got a little purse,
   Made of leathern ratchin skin;
   We want a little of your money
   To line it well within;
   For it's, etc.

4. Call up the butler of this house,
   Likewise the mistress too,
   And all the little children
   That round the table go;
   For it's, etc.

   (♩ ♪)

5. Bring us out a table
   And spread it with a cloth,
   Bring us out a mouldy cheese
   And some of your Christmas loaf;
   For it's, etc.

6. Good master and good mistress,
   While you're sitting by the fire,
   Pray think of us poor children
   That's wandered in the mire;
   For it's, etc.

46. GLOUCESTERSHIRE WASSAIL

English traditional carol
arranged by R. VAUGHAN WILLIAMS

1. Was- sail,__ was- sail,__ all o - ver the town!__ Our toast it is white, and our ale it__ is brown, Our__ bowl it__ is__ made of the white ma- ple tree; With the was - sail- ing bowl we'll drink__ to thee.

2. So here is to Cher-ry and to his right cheek,__ Pray God send our mas- ter a good piece__ of beef, And a good piece of__ beef that__ may we all see; With the was - sail- ing bowl we'll drink__ to thee.

Reprinted from *The Oxford Book of Carols* by permission

3. And here is to Dobbin and to his right eye,
   Pray God send our master a good Christmas pie,
   And a good Christmas pie that may we all see;
   With our wassailing bowl we'll drink to thee.

4. So here is to Broad May and to her broad horn,
   May God send our master a good crop of corn,
   And a good crop of corn that may we all see;
   With the wassailing bowl we'll drink to thee.

5. And here is to Fillpail and to her left ear,
   Pray God send our master a happy New Year,
   And a happy New Year as e'er he did see;
   With our wassailing bowl we'll drink to thee.

6. And here is to Colly and to her long tail,
   Pray God send our master he never may fail
   A bowl of strong beer; I pray you draw near,
   And our jolly wassail it's then you shall hear.

7. Come, butler, come fill us a bowl of the best,
   Then we|hope that your|soul in|heaven may|rest;
   But|if you do draw us a bowl of the small,
   Then down shall go butler, bowl and all.

8. Then here's to the maid in the lily white smock,
   Who tripped to the door and slipped back the lock!
   Who tripped to the door and pulled back the pin,
   For to let these jolly wassailers in.

Wassail, Wes hal, Old English, 'Be thou whole' (hale); a form of salutation, and hence a festive occasion.   Cf. 'wassail bowl', cup, or horn.

Cherry and Dobbin are horses. Broad May, Fillpail, and Colly are cows.

47. WHAT CHEER?

Words from RICHARD HILL'S
Commonplace Book (16th. c.)

WILLIAM WALTON

Now the King— of heav'n his birth hath— take, Joy and— mirth— we ought to— make; Say each to o - ther, for— his sake: 'What cheer? What cheer? What cheer? What cheer?'— 'What cheer?' I tell you all— with heart so— free: Right wel - come, wel - come, ye be to me;   Be glad___ and mer - ry, for cha - ri -

- ty! What   cheer? What   cheer? Good   cheer! Good   cheer! Be

What cheer?   What cheer?   Good cheer!   Good cheer!   Be

mer - ry and glad, ___ be mer - ry and glad, ___ be

Allargando

mer - ry and glad___ this good New___ Year! ___

48. WHEN CHRIST WAS BORN

Words anon. (15th. c.)

REGINALD JACQUES

1. When Christ_was born_ of Ma - ry free, In Beth - lem in_ that
3. This King_ is come_ to save_ his kind, ___ In _ the scrip-ture
4. Then,_dear Lord,_ for thy_great grace,___ Grant us the bliss_ to

fair ci - ty, An-gels sung e'er with mirth and glee,_
as we find; There-fore this song have we_ in mind:_ *In_ ex-cel-sis glo-ri-a.*
see thy face, Where we may sing_ to thy_ so-lace:

2. Herd-men be-held these an-gels bright-To them_ap-pear-ed with great light, And

D.C. (vv. 3 & 4)

said,_'God's son_ is born_this night':_ *In_ ex-cel-sis glo-ri-a.*

Words reprinted from *The Oxford Book of Carols* by permission

© 1961 Oxford University Press

49. WHILE SHEPHERDS WATCHED THEIR FLOCKS

Words by
NAHUM TATE (1652-1715)

Este's Psalter, 1592

1. While shep-herds watched their flocks by night, All
   seat-ed on the ground, The an-gel of the
   Lord came down, And glo-ry shone a-round.

2. 'Fear not,' said he (for might-y dread Had
   seized their troub-led mind); 'Glad ti-dings of great
   joy I bring To you and all man-kind.

3. 'To you in David's town this day
   Is born of David's line
   A Saviour, who is Christ the Lord;
   And this shall be the sign:

4. 'The heavenly Babe you there shall find
   To human view displayed,
   All meanly wrapped in swathing bands,
   And in a manger laid.'

5. Thus spake the Seraph; and forthwith
   Appeared a shining throng
   Of angels praising God, who thus
   Addressed their joyful song:

6. 'All glory be to God on high,
   And on the earth be peace;
   Good-will henceforth from heaven to men
   Begin and never cease.'

ALTERNATIVE VERSION

harmonized by T. RAVENSCROFT (1621)

It is suggested that this version be used for some verses, either by the choir alone, or with the people singing the melody. The tenor part, which has the melody, should be made prominent.

50. WHILE THE SHEPHERDS WERE WATCHING

Words by
BENEDICT ELLIS

C. ARMSTRONG GIBBS

From *A Saviour Born*, a cantata for women's voices *(O.U.P.)*
This carol in its original form (S.S.A.) is also available in the O.C.S. Series (W 13)

© 1955 Oxford University Press

Ah Ah

Ah Ah

3. Not in a bright pa - lace was young Je - sus found, But

Ah Ah

in a dim sta - ble with straw on the ground, His cra - dle a

men, And peace to you all on the earth. A - men.

men, ___ And peace to you all on the earth. ___ A - men.

men, ___ And peace to you all on the earth. ___ A - men.

men, And ___ peace to you all ___ on the earth. A - men.

To ___ these sim-ple shep-herds, to the thief ___ on the tree God

To ___ these sim-ple shep-herds, to the thief ___ on the tree God

To these sim-ple shep-herds, to the thief ___ on the tree God

To these sim-ple shep-herds, to the thief ___ on the tree ___ God ___

*Optional line for a few high sopranos

THE NINE LESSONS

The Congregation, standing, shall be bidden to Prayer in these words:

BELOVED in Christ, at this Christmas-tide let it be our care and delight to hear again the message of the angels, and in heart and mind to go even unto Bethlehem and see this thing which is come to pass, and the Babe lying in a manger.

Therefore let us read and mark in Holy Scripture the tale of the loving purposes of God from the first days of our disobedience unto the glorious Redemption brought us by this Holy Child.

But first, let us pray for the needs of the whole world; for peace on earth and goodwill among all his people; for unity and brotherhood within the Church he came to build, and especially in this our diocese.

And because this would rejoice his heart, let us remember, in his name, the poor and helpless, the cold, the hungry, and the oppressed; the sick and them that mourn, the lonely and the unloved, the aged and the little children; all those who know not the Lord Jesus, or who love him not, or who by sin have grieved his heart of love.

Lastly, let us remember before God all those who rejoice with us, but upon another shore, and in a greater light, that multitude which no man can number, whose hope was in the Word made flesh, and with whom in the Lord Jesus we are one for evermore.

These prayers and praises let us humbly offer up to the Throne of Heaven, in the words which Christ himself hath taught us:

OUR Father, which art in heaven, Hallowed be thy name; Thy kingdom come; Thy will be done; In earth as it is in heaven. Give us this day our daily bread. And forgive us our trespasses, As we forgive them that trespass against us. And lead us not into temptation; But deliver us from evil: For thine is the kingdom, The power, and the glory, For ever and ever. Amen.

Then shall the Congregation sit.
The Readers of the Lessons should be appointed after a definite order;
in a Cathedral, for instance, from a Chorister up to a Bishop.
Each Reader should proceed to the Reading Desk at the beginning of the
last verse of the preceding carol; and announce his Lesson by the descrip-
tive sentence attached to it. At the end of the Lesson, the Reader should
pause and say: Thanks be to God.

FIRST LESSON

*God announces in the Garden of Eden that the
seed of woman shall bruise the serpent's head.*

GENESIS iii

A ND they heard the voice of the Lord God walking in the garden
in the cool of the day: and Adam and his wife hid themselves
from the presence of the Lord God amongst the trees of the garden.
And the Lord God called unto Adam, and said unto him, Where
art thou? And he said, I heard thy voice in the garden, and I was
afraid, because I was naked; and I hid myself. And he said, Who
told thee that thou wast naked? Hast thou eaten of the tree, whereof
I commanded thee that thou shouldest not eat? And the man said,
The woman whom thou gavest to be with me, she gave me of the
tree, and I did eat. And the Lord God said unto the woman,
What is this that thou hast done? And the woman said, The serpent
beguiled me, and I did eat. And the Lord God said unto the serpent,
Because thou hast done this, thou art cursed above all cattle, and
above every beast of the field; upon thy belly shalt thou go, and
dust shalt thou eat all the days of thy life: and I will put enmity
between thee and the woman, and between thy seed and her seed;
it shall bruise thy head, and thou shalt bruise his heel.

SECOND LESSON

*God promises to faithful Abraham that in his
seed shall the nations of the earth be blessed.*

GENESIS xxii

A ND the angel of the Lord called unto Abraham out of heaven
the second time, and said, By myself have I sworn, saith the
Lord, for because thou hast done this thing, and hast not withheld
thy son, thine only son: that in blessing I will bless thee, and in
multiplying I will multiply thy seed as the stars of the heaven, and
as the sand which is upon the sea shore; and thy seed shall possess
the gate of his enemies; and in thy seed shall all the nations of the
earth be blessed; because thou hast obeyed my voice.

THIRD LESSON

Christ's birth and kingdom are foretold by Isaiah.

ISAIAH ix

THE people that walked in darkness have seen a great light: they that dwell in the land of the shadow of death, upon them hath the light shined. For unto us a child is born, unto us a son is given: and the government shall be upon his shoulder: and his name shall be called Wonderful, Counsellor, the mighty God, the everlasting Father, the Prince of Peace. Of the increase of his government and peace there shall be no end, upon the throne of David, and upon his kingdom, to order it, and to establish it with judgment and with justice from henceforth even for ever. The zeal of the Lord of hosts will perform this.

FOURTH LESSON

The peace that Christ will bring is foreshown.

ISAIAH xi

AND there shall come forth a rod out of the stem of Jesse, and a branch shall grow out of his roots: and the spirit of the Lord shall rest upon him, the spirit of wisdom and understanding, the spirit of counsel and might, the spirit of knowledge and of the fear of the Lord; and shall make him of quick understanding in the fear of the Lord. With righteousness shall he judge the poor, and reprove with equity for the meek of the earth. The wolf also shall dwell with the lamb, and the leopard shall lie down with the kid; and the calf and the young lion and the fatling together; and a little child shall lead them. And the cow and the bear shall feed; their young ones shall lie down together: and the lion shall eat straw like the ox. And the sucking child shall play on the hole of the asp, and the weaned child shall put his hand on the cockatrice' den. They shall not hurt nor destroy in all my holy mountain: for the earth shall be full of the knowledge of the Lord, as the waters cover the sea.

ALTERNATIVE FOURTH LESSON

The prophet Micah foretells the glory of little Bethlehem.

MICAH v

B UT thou, Beth-lehem Ephratah, though thou be little among the thousands of Judah, yet out of thee shall he come forth unto me that is to be ruler in Israel; whose goings forth have been from of old, from everlasting. Therefore will he give them up, until the time that she which travaileth hath brought forth: then the remnant of his brethren shall return unto the children of Israel. And he shall stand and feed in the strength of the Lord, in the majesty of the name of the Lord his God; and they shall abide: for now shall he be great unto the ends of the earth.

FIFTH LESSON

The angel Gabriel salutes the Blessed Virgin Mary.

ST LUKE i

A ND in the sixth month the angel Gabriel was sent from God unto a city of Galilee, named Nazareth, to a virgin espoused to a man whose name was Joseph, of the house of David; and the virgin's name was Mary. And the angel came in unto her, and said, Hail, thou that art highly favoured, the Lord is with thee: blessed art thou among women. And when she saw him, she was troubled at his saying, and cast in her mind what manner of salutation this should be. And the angel said unto her, Fear not, Mary: for thou hast found favour with God. And, behold, thou shalt conceive in thy womb, and bring forth a son, and shalt call his name JESUS. He shall be great, and shall be called the Son of the Highest: and the Lord God shall give unto him the throne of his father David: and he shall reign over the house of Jacob for ever; and of his kingdom there shall be no end. Then said Mary unto the angel, How shall this be, seeing I know not a man? And the angel answered and said unto her, The Holy Ghost shall come upon thee, and the power of the Highest shall overshadow thee: therefore also that holy thing which shall be born of thee shall be called the Son of God. And Mary said, Behold the handmaid of the Lord; be it unto me according to thy word. And the angel departed from her.

Alternative fifth lesson – see overleaf

ALTERNATIVE FIFTH LESSON

The prophet in exile foresees the coming of the glory of the Lord.

ISAIAH LX

A RISE, shine; for thy light is come, and the glory of the Lord is risen upon thee. For, behold, the darkness shall cover the earth, and gross darkness the people: but the Lord shall arise upon thee, and his glory shall be seen upon thee. And the Gentiles shall come to thy light, and kings to the brightness of thy rising. Lift up thine eyes round about, and see: all they gather themselves together, they come to thee: thy sons shall come from far, and thy daughters shall be nursed at thy side. Then thou shalt see, and flow together, and thine heart shall fear, and be enlarged; because the abundance of the sea shall be converted unto thee, the forces of the Gentiles shall come unto thee. The multitude of camels shall cover thee, the dromedaries of Midian and Ephah; all they from Sheba shall come: they shall bring gold and incense; and they shall shew forth the praises of the Lord. The sun shall be no more thy light by day; neither for brightness shall the moon give light unto thee: but the Lord shall be unto thee an everlasting light, and thy God thy glory.

SIXTH LESSON

St Matthew tells of the birth of Jesus.

ST MATTHEW i

Now the birth of Jesus Christ was on this wise: When as his mother Mary was espoused to Joseph, before they came together, she was found with child of the Holy Ghost. Then Joseph her husband, being a just man, and not willing to make her a publick example, was minded to put her away privily. But while he thought on these things, behold, the angel of the Lord appeared unto him in a dream, saying, Joseph, thou son of David, fear not to take unto thee Mary thy wife: for that which is conceived in her is of the Holy Ghost. And she shall bring forth a son, and thou shalt call his name JESUS: for he shall save his people from their sins. Now all this was done, that it might be fulfilled which was spoken of the Lord by the prophet, saying, Behold, a virgin shall be with child, and shall bring forth a son, and they shall call his name Emmanuel, which being interpreted is, God with us.

ALTERNATIVE SIXTH LESSON

St Luke tells of the birth of Jesus.

ST LUKE ii

And it came to pass in those days, that there went out a decree from Cæsar Augustus, that all the world should be taxed. And all went to be taxed, every one into his own city. And Joseph also went up from Galilee, out of the city of Nazareth, into Judæa, unto the city of David, which is called Bethlehem; (because he was of the house and lineage of David:) to be taxed with Mary his espoused wife, being great with child. And so it was, that, while they were there, the days were accomplished that she should be delivered. And she brought forth her firstborn son, and wrapped him in swaddling clothes, and laid him in a manger; because there was no room for them in the inn.

SEVENTH LESSON

The shepherds go to the manger.

ST LUKE ii

A ND there were in the same country shepherds abiding in the field, keeping watch over their flock by night. And, lo, the angel of the Lord came upon them, and the glory of the Lord shone round about them: and they were sore afraid. And the angel said unto them, Fear not: for, behold, I bring you good tidings of great joy, which shall be to all people. For unto you is born this day in the city of David a Saviour, which is Christ the Lord. And this shall be a sign unto you; Ye shall find the babe wrapped in swaddling clothes, lying in a manger. And suddenly there was with the angel a multitude of the heavenly host praising God, and saying, Glory to God in the highest, and on earth peace, good will toward men. And it came to pass, as the angels were gone away from them into heaven, the shepherds said one to another, Let us now go even unto Bethlehem, and see this thing which is come to pass, which the Lord hath made known unto us. And they came with haste, and found Mary, and Joseph, and the babe lying in a manger.

EIGHTH LESSON

The wise men are led by the star to Jesus.

ST MATTHEW ii

N ow when Jesus was born in Bethlehem of Judæa in the days of Herod the king, behold, there came wise men from the east to Jerusalem, saying, Where is he that is born King of the Jews? for we have seen his star in the east, and are come to worship him. When Herod the king had heard these things, he was troubled, and all Jerusalem with him. And when he had gathered all the chief priests and scribes of the people together, he demanded of them where Christ should be born. And they said unto him, In Bethlehem of Judæa: for thus it is written by the prophet, And thou Bethlehem in the land of Juda, art not the least among the princes of Juda: for out of thee shall come a Governor, that shall rule my people Israel. Then Herod, when he had privily called the wise men, inquired of them diligently what time the star appeared. And he sent them to Bethlehem, and said, Go and search diligently for the young child; and when ye have found him, bring me word again, that I may come and worship him also. When they had heard the king, they departed; and lo, the star, which they saw in the east, went before them, till it came and stood over where the young child was. When they saw the star, they rejoiced with exceeding great joy. And when they were come into the house, they saw the young child with Mary his mother, and fell down, and worshipped him: and when they had opened their treasures, they presented unto him gifts, gold, and frankincense, and myrrh.

The Congregation shall stand for the ninth lesson.

NINTH LESSON

St John unfolds the great mystery of the Incarnation.

ST JOHN i

IN the beginning was the Word, and the Word was with God, and the Word was God. The same was in the beginning with God. All things were made by him; and without him was not any thing made that was made. In him was life; and the life was the light of men. And the light shineth in darkness; and the darkness comprehended it not. There was a man sent from God, whose name was John. The same came for a witness, to bear witness of the light, that all men through him might believe. He was not that light, but was sent to bear witness of that light. That was the true light, which lighteth every man that cometh into the world. He was in the world, and the world was made by him, and the world knew him not. He came unto his own, and his own received him not. But as many as received him, to them gave he power to become the sons of God, even to them that believe on his name: which were born, not of blood, nor of the will of the flesh, nor of the will of man, but of God. And the Word was made flesh, and dwelt among us, (and we beheld his glory, the glory as of the only-begotten of the Father,) full of grace and truth.

Priest.   The Lord be with you.
Answer.   And with thy spirit.
Priest.   Let us pray.

All kneel.

THE COLLECT FOR CHRISTMAS EVE

O GOD, who makest us glad with the yearly remembrance of the birth of thy only Son, Jesus Christ: Grant that as we joyfully receive him for our redeemer, so we may with sure confidence behold him, when he shall come to be our judge; who liveth and reigneth with thee and the Holy Ghost, one God, world without end. *Amen.*

Or,

THE COLLECT FOR CHRISTMAS DAY

A LMIGHTY GOD, who hast given us thy only-begotten Son to take our nature upon him, and as at this time to be born of a pure Virgin: Grant that we being regenerate, and made thy children by adoption and grace, may daily be renewed by thy Holy Spirit; through the same our Lord Jesus Christ, who liveth and reigneth with thee and the same Spirit, ever one God, world without end. *Amen.*

THE BLESSING

M AY he who by his Incarnation gathered into one things earthly and heavenly, fill you with the sweetness of inward peace and goodwill; and the blessing of God Almighty, the Father, the Son, and the Holy Ghost, be upon you and remain with you always. *Amen.*